Karl
kins

TE DEUM

for chorus, two trumpets, timpani,
percussion & string orchestra

Vocal score

BOOSEY &HAWKES

Boosey & Hawkes Music Publishers Ltd
www.boosey.com

Published by Boosey & Hawkes Music Publishers Ltd
Aldwych House
71–91 Aldwych
London
WC2B 4HN

www.boosey.com

ISMN 979-0-060-12031-2
ISBN 978-0-85162-597-3

First impression 2009. Second impression 2016, with corrections

Printed by Halstan:
Halstan UK, 2–10 Plantation Road, Amersham, Bucks, HP6 6HJ. United Kingdom
Halstan DE, Weißliliengasse 4, 55116 Mainz. Germany

Music origination by New Notations London
Cover design: design united worldwide
Cover photo: istock

For the Liverpool Welsh Choral: composed to celebrate
Liverpool's year as the European Capital of Culture 2008

First performed on 30 November 2008 at Philharmonic Hall, Liverpool,
by Liverpool Welsh Choral and the Royal Liverpool Philharmonic Orchestra,
conducted by the composer

First recording: EMI CD 50999 6 46430 2 1,
by the National Youth Choir of Great Britain
and the London Symphony Orchestra,
conducted by the composer

Te Deum laudamus: te Dominum confitemur.

Te aeternum Patrem omnis terra veneratur.

Tibi omnes angeli; tibi caeli et universae potestates;

tibi cherubim et seraphim incessabili voce proclamant:

Sanctus, Sanctus, Sanctus, Dominus Deus Sabaoth.

Pleni sunt caeli et terra majestatis gloriae tuae.

Te gloriosus apostolorum chorus,

Te prophetarum laudabilis numerus,

Te martyrum candidatus laudat exercitus.

Te per orbem terrarum sancta confitetur Ecclesia,

Patrem immensae majestatis:

venerandum tuum verum et unicum Filium;

Sanctum quoque Paraclitum, Spiritum.

Tu Rex gloriae, Christe.

Tu Patris sempiternus es Filius.

Tu ad liberandum suscepturus hominem,

   non horruisti Virginis uterum.

Tu, devicto mortis aculeo,

   aperuisti credentibus regna caelorum.

Tu ad dexteram Dei sedes, in gloria Patris.

Judex crederis esse venturus.

Te ergo quaesumus, tuis famulis subveni,

   quos pretioso sanguine redemisti.

Aeterna fac cum sanctis tuis in gloria numerari.

Salvum fac populum tuum, Domine, et benedic hereditati tuae.

Et rege eos, et extolle illos usque in aeternum.

Per singulos dies benedicimus te;

et laudamus nomen tuum in saeculum, et in saeculum saeculi.

Dignare, Domine, die isto sine peccato nos custodire.

Miserere nostri, Domine, miserere nostri.

Fiat misericordia tua, Domine, super nos,

   quemadmodum speravimus in te.

In te, Domine, speravi: non confundar in aeternum.

We praise you O God: we acknowledge you to be the Lord.

All the earth now worships you, the Father everlasting.

To you all angels cry aloud, the heavens and all the powers therein;

to you cherubim and seraphim continually do cry:

Holy, Holy, Holy, Lord God of Sabaoth.

Heaven and earth are full of the majesty of your glory.

The glorious company of the apostles praise you,

the goodly fellowship of the prophets praise you,

the noble army of martyrs praise you,

the holy Church throughout all the world acknowledges you,

the Father of an infinite majesty:

your adorable, true, and only Son;

also the Holy Spirit, the counsellor.

You are the King of glory, O Christ.

You are the everlasting Son of the Father.

When you took upon yourself to deliver man

> *you did not disdain the Virgin's womb.*

When you had overcome the sharpness of death

> *you opened the kingdom of heaven to all believers.*

You sit at the right hand of God in the glory of the Father.

We believe that you will come to be our judge.

We therefore pray you help your servants,

> *whom you have redeemed with your precious blood.*

Make them to be numbered with your saints in glory everlasting.

O Lord save your people and bless your heritage.

Govern them and lift them up forever.

Day by day we magnify you,

and we worship your name, world without end.

Vouchsafe, O Lord, to keep us this day without sin.

O Lord have mercy upon us, have mercy upon us.

O Lord, let your mercy be upon us,

> *as our trust is in you.*

O Lord, in you have I trusted: let me never be confounded.

INSTRUMENTATION

2 Trumpets in C
Timpani
Percussion (4)★
Strings

★1: glockenspiel, xylophone
2: bass drum
3: cymbals, suspended cymbal
4: side drum

Duration: 15 minutes

Performance materials available on hire

TE DEUM

KARL JENKINS
(b 1944)

18976

*Sing upper notes if lower notes out of range

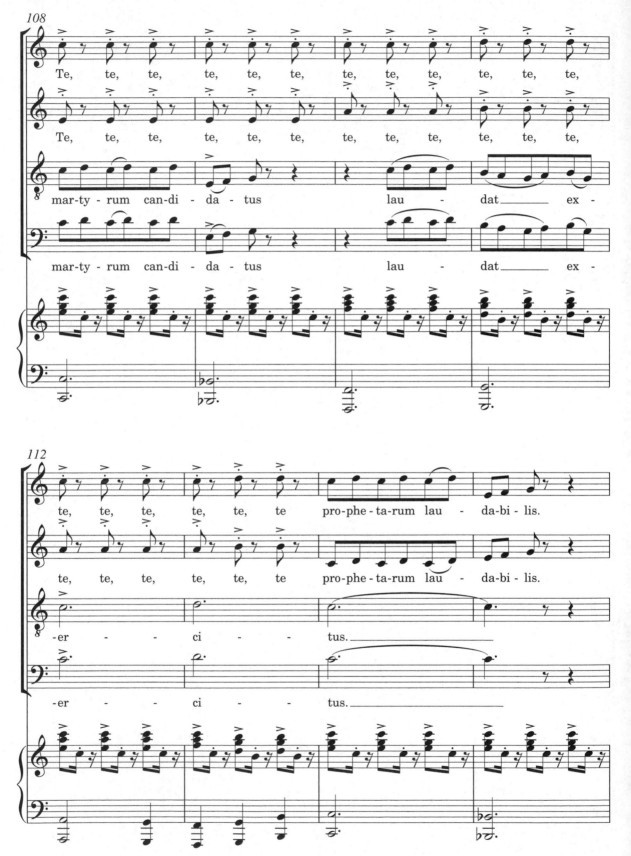

14

18

18976

28

nos cus - to - di - re.

stringendo al fine
(ad lib)